THESEUS
AND THE
MINOTAUR

retold by Nel Yomtov

illustrated by Tod Smith

coloured by Dave Gutierrez

www.raintreepublishers.co.uk
Visit our website to find out
more information about
Raintree books.

To order:
☎ Phone +44 (0) 1865 888066
🖷 Fax +44 (0) 1865 314091
🖳 Visit www.raintreepublishers.co.uk

Raintree is an imprint of Capstone Global Library Limited, a company incorporated in England
and Wales having its registered office at 7 Pilgrim Street, London, EC4V 6LB – Registered
company number: 6695582

"Raintree" is a registered trademark of Pearson Education Limited, under licence to Capstone
Global Library Limited

Text © Stone Arch Books 2009
First published by Stone Arch Books in 2009
First published in hardback and paperback in the United Kingdom by Capstone Global Library
in 2010
The moral rights of the proprietor have been asserted.

Edited in the UK by Diyan Leake
Originated by Capstone Global Library Ltd
Printed in China by Leo Paper Products Ltd

ISBN 978 1 406 21425 3 (hardback)
14 13 12 11 10
10 9 8 7 6 5 4 3 2 1

ISBN 978 1 406 21430 7 (paperback)
14 13 12 11 10
10 9 8 7 6 5 4 3 2 1

British Library Cataloguing in Publication Data
Yomtov, Nel -- Theseus and the Minotaur
A full catalogue record for this book is available from the British Library.

Contents

INTRODUCING...

THESEUS

ARIADNE

KING AEGEUS

THE
MINOTAUR

MEDEA

Many years passed. King Aegeus finally had a son ...

You are a lively one, boy!

... but not the son that the Oracle had promised.

And handsome, like his father, husband.

Medea, my queen. Our son grows stronger every day.

12

15

Having done another brave deed,
Theseus set off again toward Athens. 23

Later, at King Aegeus's palace ...

My powers tell me that the blonde-haired stranger is a spy ...

...sent here to kill you!

A spy?!

Yes, but I have a plan.

I will send guards to find the stranger.

They will invite him to tonight's feast.

32

35

Time passed, and Prince Theseus performed many brave deeds.

But none were braver than slaying the giant white bull.

The huge creature was the son of Poseidon, the god of the sea.

The bull had terrorized all of Greece for many years.

King Aegeus sent many men to slay the great beast … and just as many had been killed.

On the day that Theseus killed the bull …

There is much you need to know about the fierce bull …

… and the pain it has brought to the people of Athens.

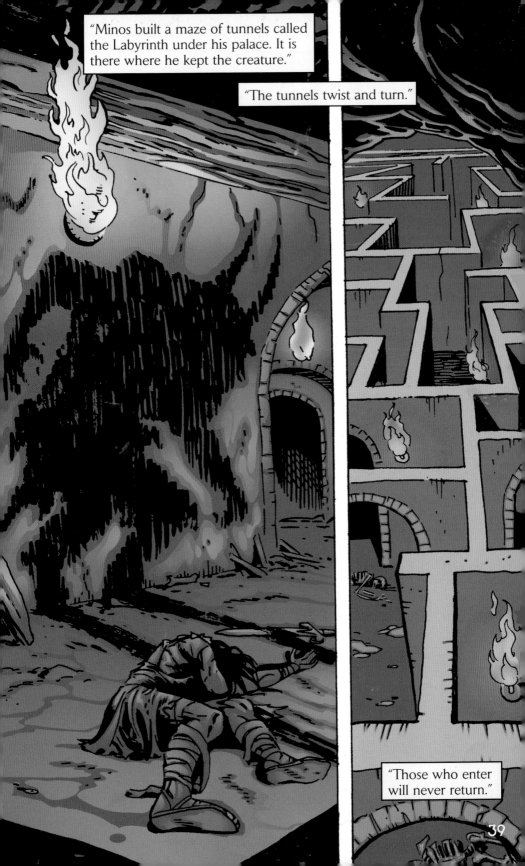

"Minos built a maze of tunnels called the Labyrinth under his palace. It is there where he kept the creature."

"The tunnels twist and turn."

"Those who enter will never return."

41

The ship's fourteen unlucky youths sailed for Crete …

… where they were to be fed to the Minotaur.

Days later, the ship arrived in Crete. King Minos was there to meet Theseus.

You wanted to see the famous prince of Athens, Ariadne.

Is he everything you expected, daughter?

45

55

KRONG!
KRONG!
KRONG!
KRONG!

Ariadne! Take their key and free my friends! Quickly!

This is the fastest way back to your ship! Hurry!

At the harbour …

I promised you freedom, my love, and now you must take me with you.

Y-yes, of course.

What have I done? I don't love Ariadne.

Why did I make such a foolish promise?

57

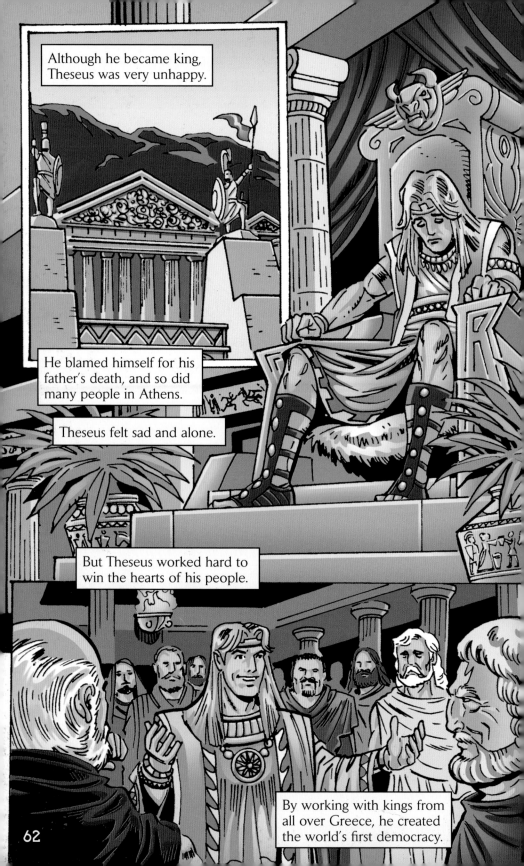

Although he became king, Theseus was very unhappy.

He blamed himself for his father's death, and so did many people in Athens.

Theseus felt sad and alone.

But Theseus worked hard to win the hearts of his people.

By working with kings from all over Greece, he created the world's first democracy.

And to this day, no one will ever forget the battle between Theseus and the Minotaur.

HOW TO PRONOUNCE GREEK NAMES

NAME	PRONUNCIATION
Aegeus	eh-JEE-uss
Aethra	EETH-ra
Ariadne	ah-ree-AD-nee
Corinth	KOR-inth
Delphi	DEL-fee
Labyrinth	LAB-ih-rinth
Medea	med-AY-a
Medus	MED-uss
Megara	MEH-ga-ra
Minos	MY-noss
Minotaur	MY-no-tawr
Naxos	NAX-oss
Periphetes	pe-ri-FEE-teeze
Pittheus	pea-TAY-uss
Poseidon	po-SIGH-dun
Sciron	SIGH-ron
Siris	SEE-riss
Theseus	THEECE-ee-uss
Troezen	TROY-zen
Zeus	ZOOCE

GLOSSARY

creature living being, human or animal

deeds things that are done or need to be done

democracy government that makes decisions through votes

harbour place where ships stay or unload their cargo

heir person who is given something upon the death of a friend or relative

oracle person who learns about the future by communicating with the gods

sacrifice something offered to the gods

sorceress woman who practises sorcery

sorcery magic involving spirits

toll charge or tax paid for passage through a bridge or road

torch flaming light that can be carried in the hand

villain wicked or evil person

THE ORACLE AT DELPHI

Have you ever seen television programmes about psychics, people who can see into the future? Believe it or not, the Greeks had psychics too! They were called the Pythia and their leader was called the Oracle. The Pythia were priestesses of Apollo, the god of the sun, in Delphi, Greece. People from all over Greece would visit the Delphic Oracle in hopes of getting a glimpse of the future.

Legend says that Delphi was originally the home of a giant python. Apollo killed the massive serpent and claimed the land as his own, making it a holy site where the Oracle at Delphi would reside. A temple was placed directly on top of a crack in the Earth where odd things had been happening. This is where the Pythia, named after the great python that once lived there, gave their predictions.

When a visitor came to inquire about the future, the Pythia would go downstairs and sit upon a chair placed directly over the crack in the Earth. After sitting there for a while, they would give their prophecies. Most of the time, the Pythia's predictions were vague or impossible to understand. So, other priests would interpret what they said. But really, the priests just made up their own predictions and simply pretended to interpret.

So why did people who went near the crack in the Earth act so strangely? The Greeks thought that this weird behaviour meant they had spoken with Apollo through the crack, giving them insight into the future. However, an American archaeologist named John Hale thinks that methane gas leaked out of the crack that the temple was built upon. Long ago, goats that grazed in Delphi would act very strangely when they neared the area. The methane gas may have made them intoxicated, or "drunk" on the gas vapours. This same gas probably made the Pythia act strangely and speak in ways that could not be understood, and it probably affected the priests who interpreted their prophecies too.

For several centuries, the Oracle at Delphi played an important role for rulers across the world. But after a few centuries, fewer people visited the Oracle. No one knows for certain why people stopped visiting, but some archaeologists believe that the crack in the Earth stopped leaking methane gas, which made the experience of visiting the Oracle less convincing.

DISCUSSION QUESTIONS

1. Theseus had promised to take Ariadne back to Athens with him, but instead he abandoned her on an island. How did his behaviour make you feel? What would have been the right thing to do if he didn't love her?

2. Is Theseus responsible for his father's death? Why or why not?

3. Ariadne gave Theseus a ball of string to use to find his way out of the Labyrinth. What are some other ways he could have kept track of his location?

WRITING PROMPTS

1. Deep in the Labyrinth, Theseus comes across the beast-like Minotaur. Imagine you're venturing through the corridors of a Labyrinth. What strange creature awaits you? What does it look like? Write about your encounter.

2. On page 13, Medea's chariot is pulled by odd-looking creatures. Write a story explaining how she came to be in possession of such a strange form of transport.

3. Theseus is visited by the famous hero Hercules. If you could be visited by any person who has ever lived, who would you choose? What would the two of you do together? Write about it.

BOOKS IN THE SERIES

Jason and the Golden Fleece

Brave Jason comes to claim his throne, but the old king will not give up his rule so easily. To prove his worth, Jason must find the greatest treasure in the world, the Golden Fleece.

Perseus and Medusa

Young Perseus grows up, unaware of his royal birth. Before he can claim his heritage, the hero is ordered to slay a hideous monster named Medusa, whose gaze turns men into solid stone. How can the youth fight an enemy he cannot even look at?

The Adventures of Hercules

The son of a mortal woman and the king of the gods, Hercules is blessed with extraordinary strength. The goddess Hera commands that the mighty Hercules must undergo twelve incredible tasks to pay for a mistake he made in the past.

Theseus and the Minotaur

The evil king of Crete demands that fourteen young Athenians be fed to the Minotaur, a half-man, half-bull. Only Prince Theseus can save them from the fearsome monster that lives deep in the maze-like Labyrinth.

FIND OUT MORE

Websites

http://www.ancientgreece.co.uk/
Visit this British Museum site to find out more about ancient Greek civilization.

http://www.bbc.co.uk/schools/primaryhistory/ancient_greeks/
This site will help you to discover still more about how the ancient Greeks lived and worked. Click on the "Gods and Heroes" link for more fun facts about Greek heroes.

http://greece.mrdonn.org/greekgods/index.html
Find out about the roles and relationships of the ancient Greek gods. The Roman names for some of them are also given on this web page.

Books

Ancient Greece (New Explore History series), Jane Shuter (Heinemann Library, 2007)

Ancient Greece (Time Travel Guides series), Anna Claybourne (Raintree, 2008)

The Ancient Greeks (Understanding People in the Past series), Rosemary Rees (Heinemann Library, 2007)

The History and Activities of Ancient Greece (Hands-on Ancient History series), Greg Owens (Heinemann Library, 2007)